Anatomy of the Human Body

Anatomy of the Human Body

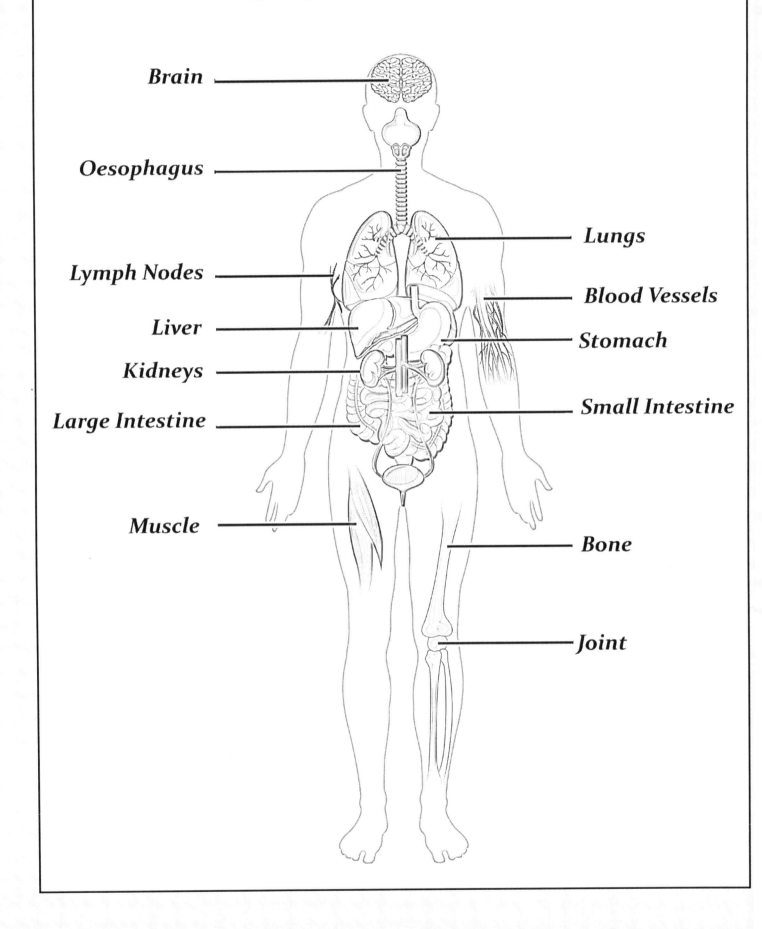

Brain

Oesophagus

Lymph Nodes

Liver

Kidneys

Large Intestine

Muscle

Lungs

Blood Vessels

Stomach

Small Intestine

Bone

Joint

Human Skeletal System

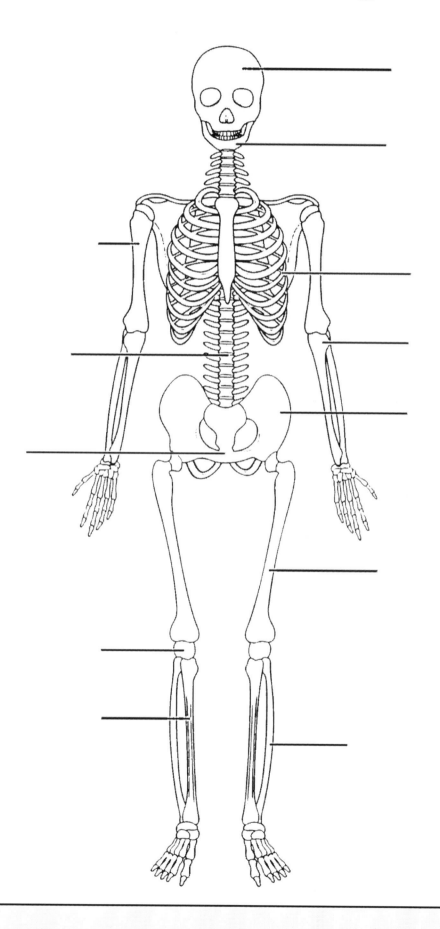

Human Skeletal System

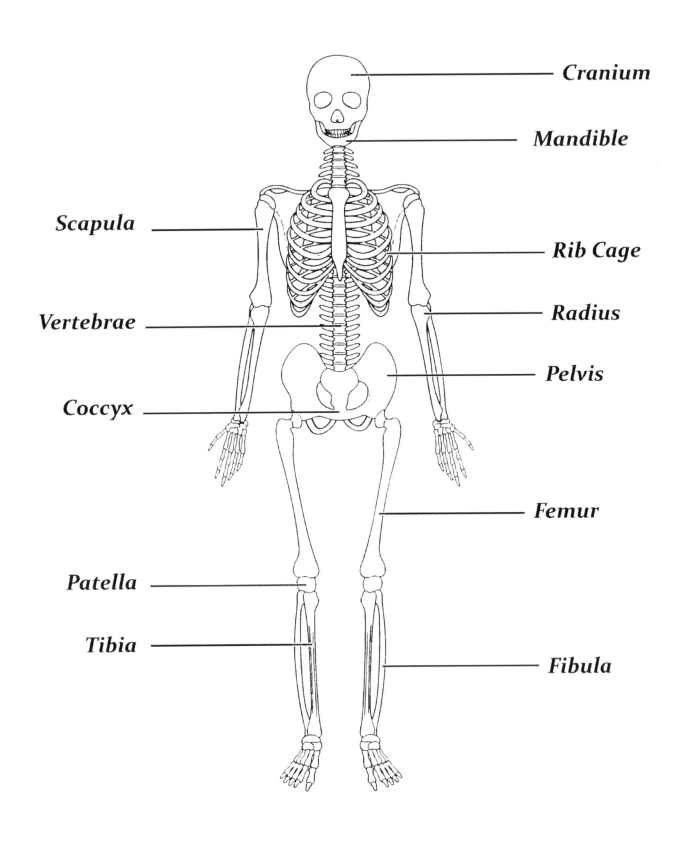

Cranium

Mandible

Scapula

Rib Cage

Radius

Vertebrae

Pelvis

Coccyx

Femur

Patella

Tibia

Fibula

Human Muscle Anatomy

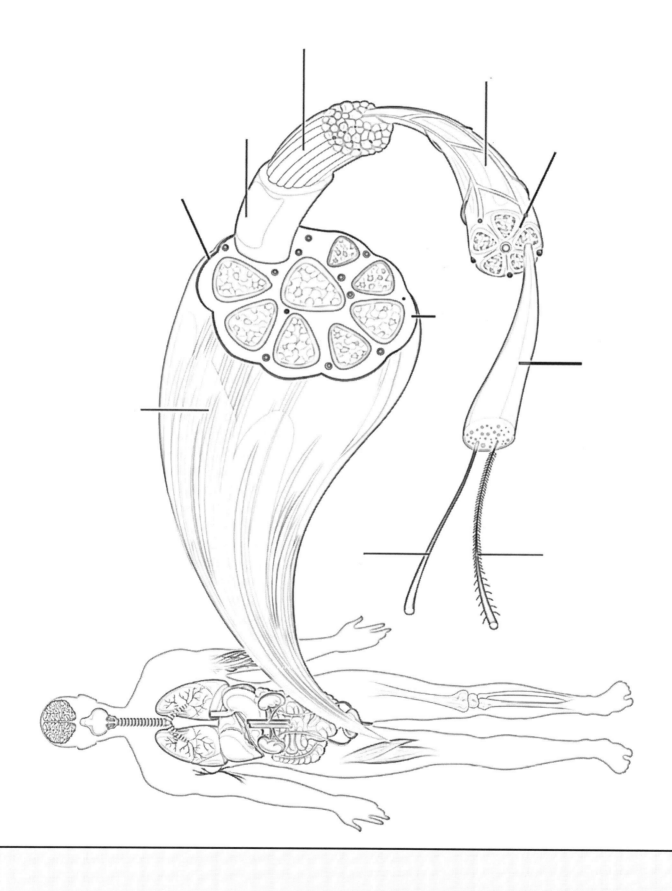

Human Muscle Anatomy

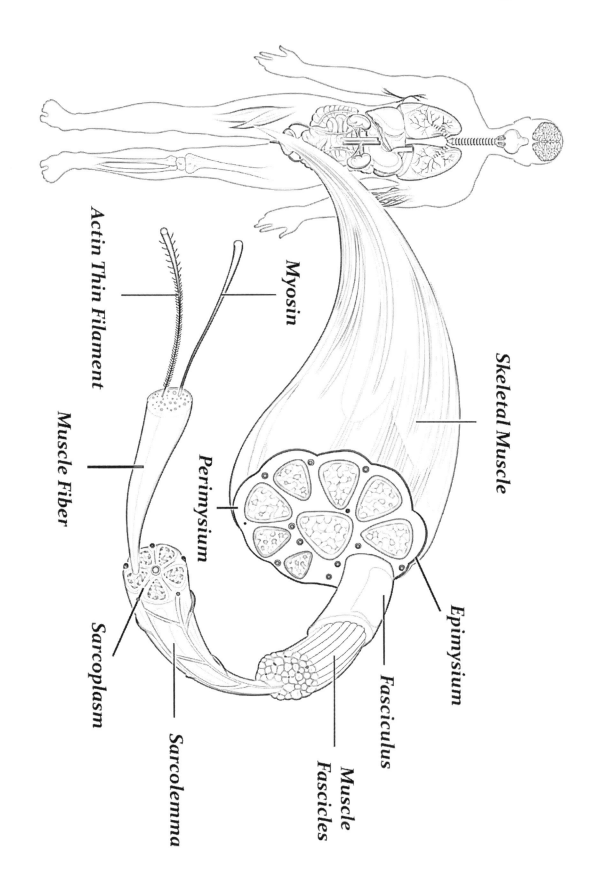

Actin Thin Filament

Myosin

Muscle Fiber

Perimysium

Skeletal Muscle

Sarcoplasm

Sarcolemma

Epimysium

Fasciculus

Muscle
Fascicles

Type of Muscle Cells

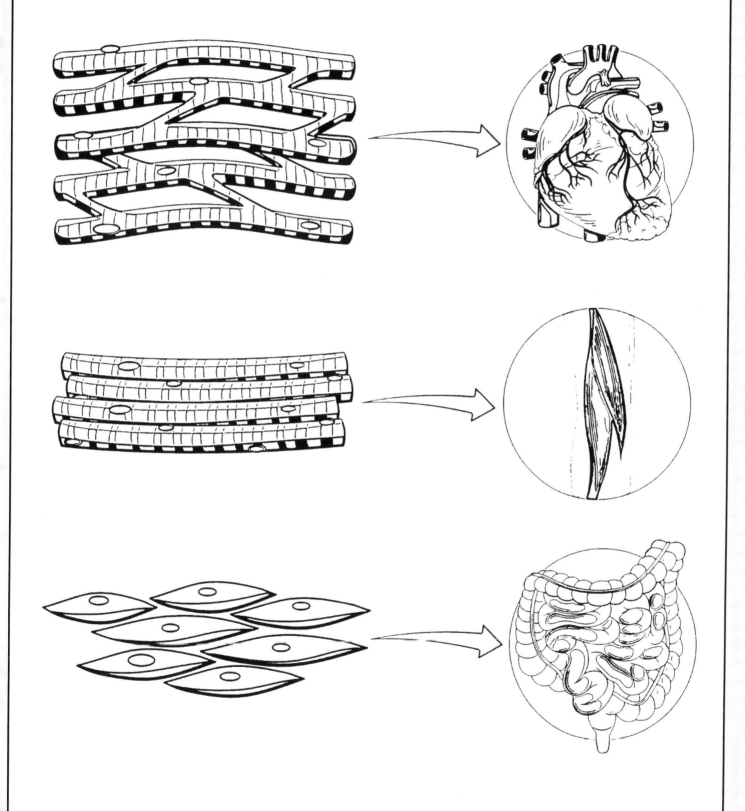

Type of Muscle Cells

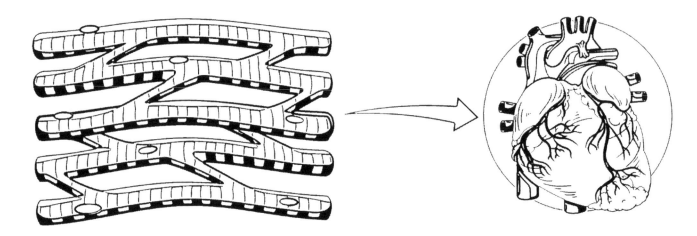

Cardiac Muscle

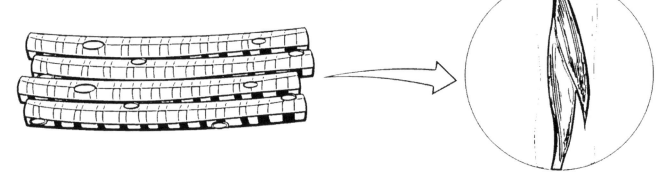

Skeletal Muscle

Smooth Muscle

Blood Flow of the Human Heart

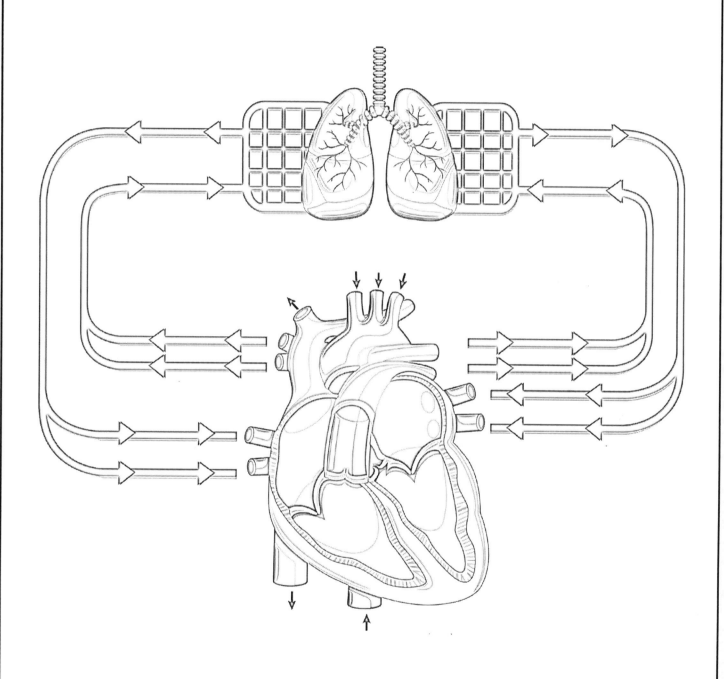

Blood Flow of the Human Heart

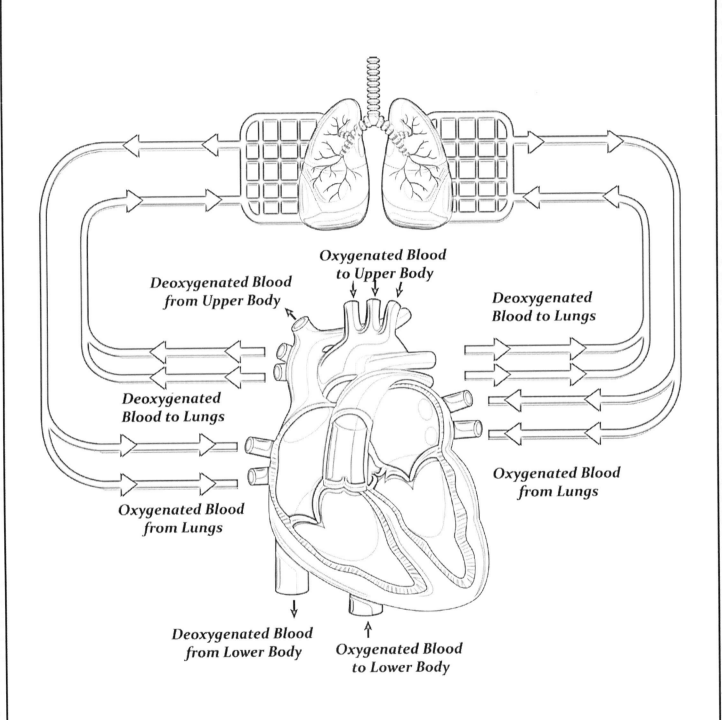

Deoxygenated Blood
from Upper Body

Oxygenated Blood
to Upper Body

Deoxygenated
Blood to Lungs

Deoxygenated
Blood to Lungs

Oxygenated Blood
from Lungs

Oxygenated Blood
from Lungs

Deoxygenated Blood
from Lower Body

Oxygenated Blood
to Lower Body

The Heart

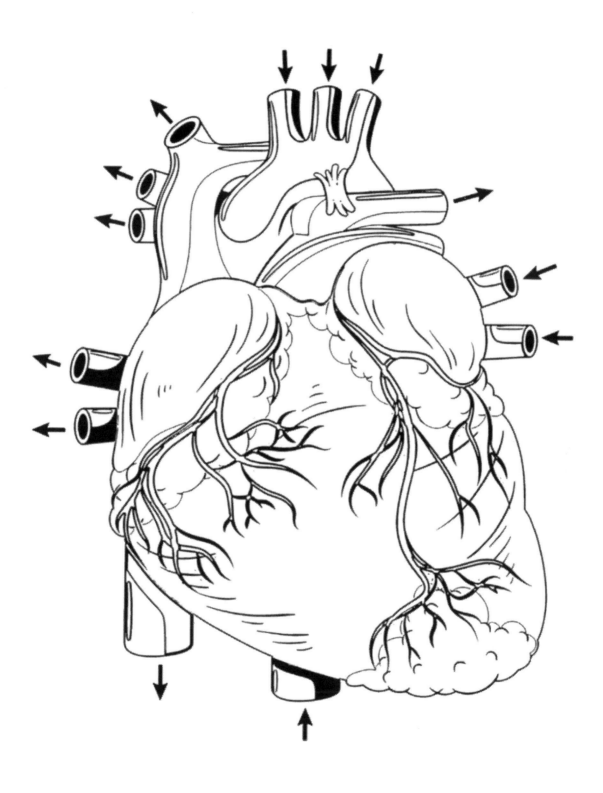

The Heart

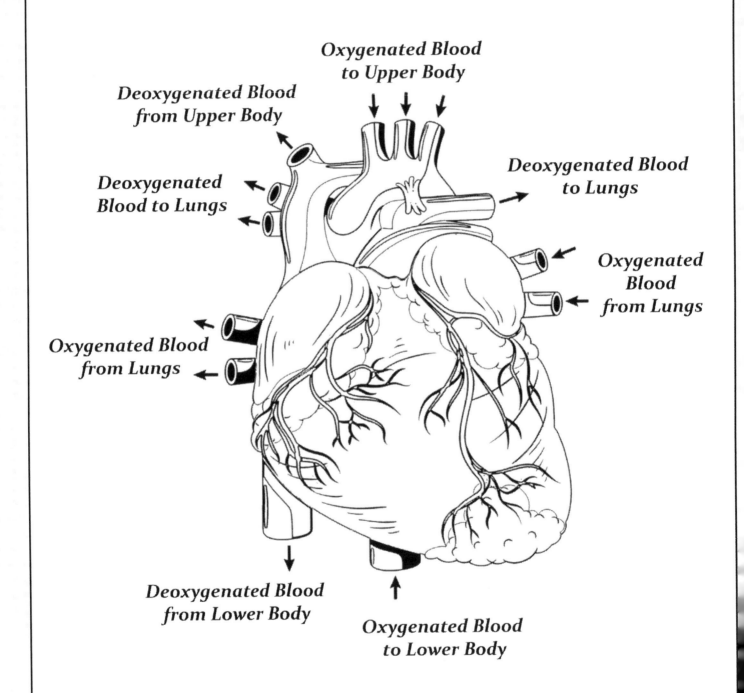

Human Nervous System

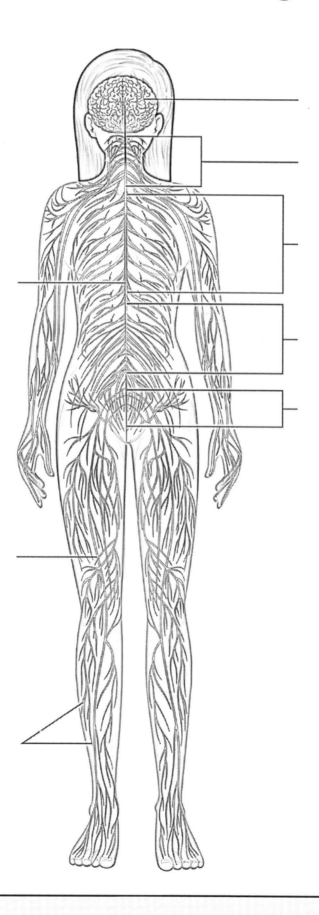

Human Nervous System

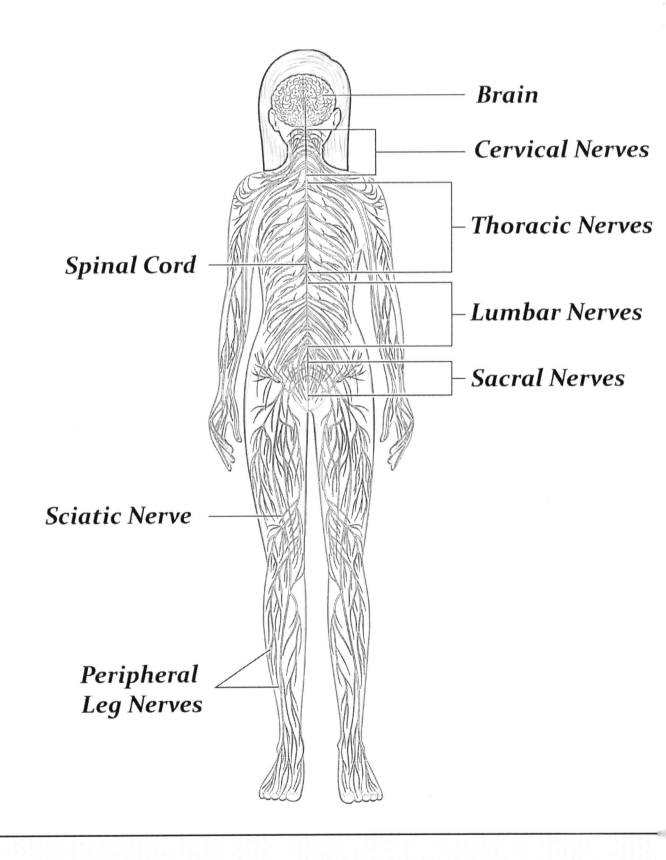

Brain

Cervical Nerves

Thoracic Nerves

Spinal Cord

Lumbar Nerves

Sacral Nerves

Sciatic Nerve

Peripheral
Leg Nerves

Parts of the Human Brain

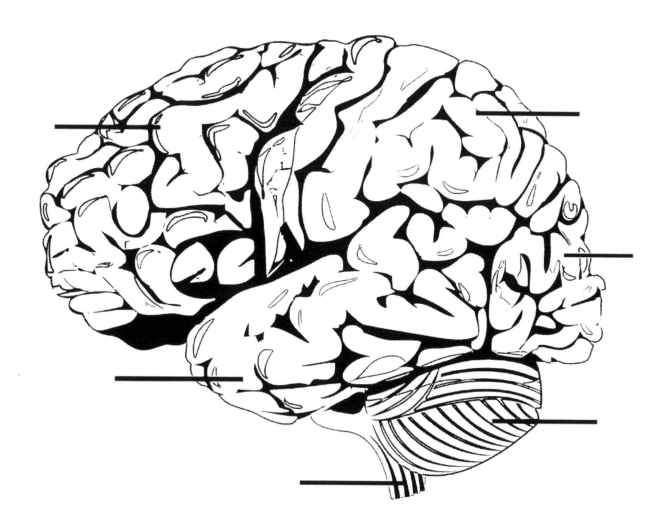

Parts of the Human Brain

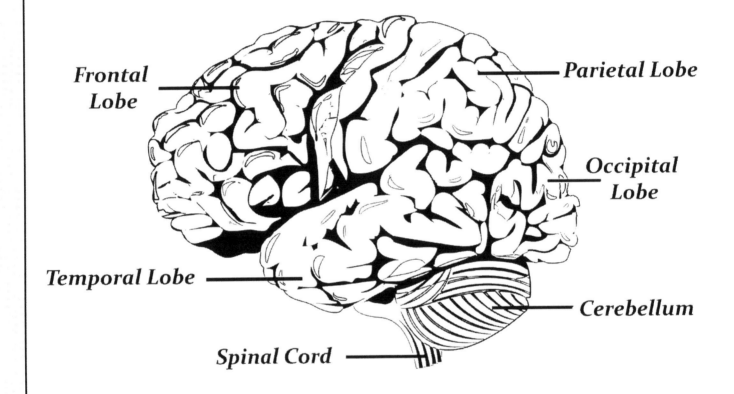

Frontal Lobe

Parietal Lobe

Occipital Lobe

Temporal Lobe

Cerebellum

Spinal Cord

Alzheimer

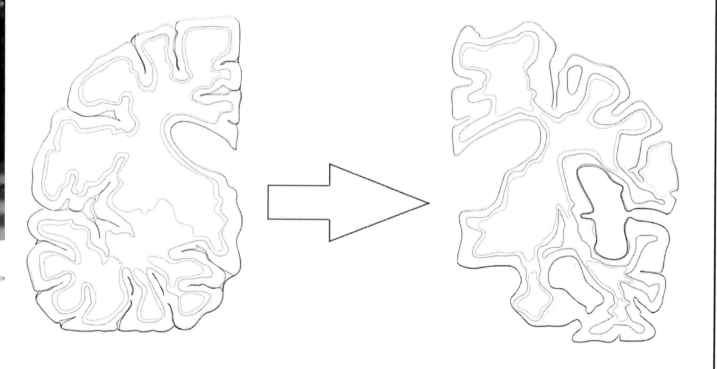

Alzheimer

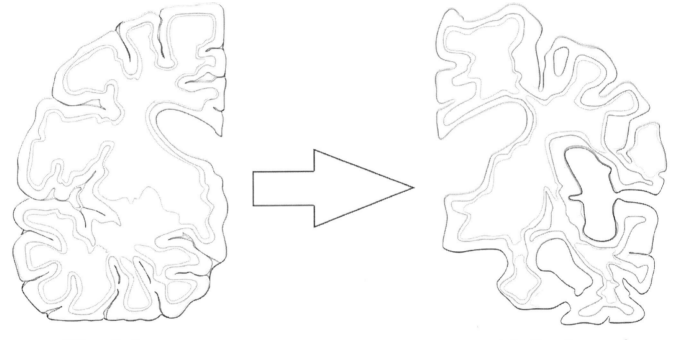

Healthy Brain

Alzheimer's Desease

Neuron Anatomy

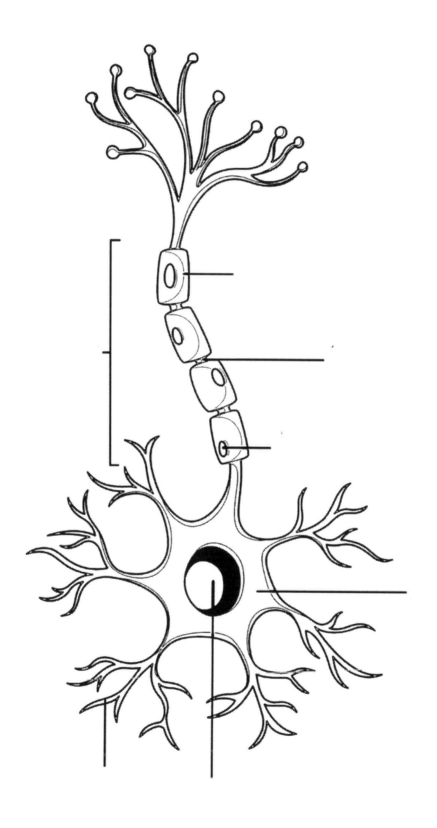

Neuron Anatomy

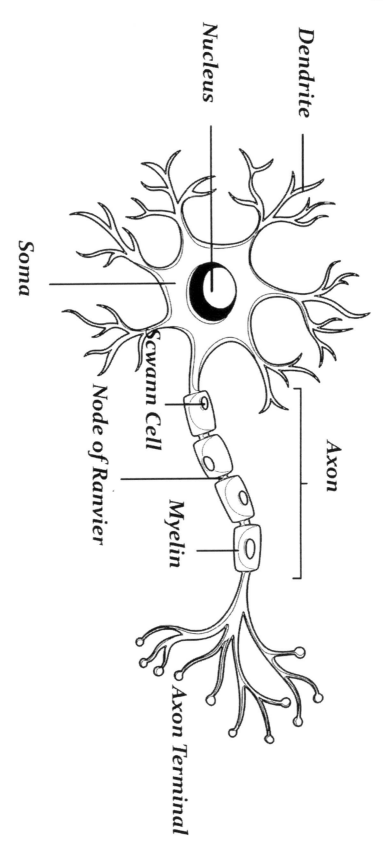

Dendrite

Nucleus

Soma

Schwann Cell

Node of Ranvier

Myelin

Axon

Axon Terminal

Human Eye Anatomy

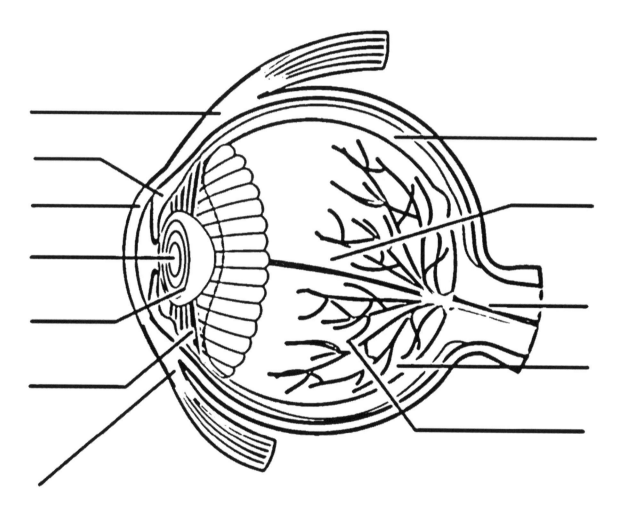

Human Eye Anatomy

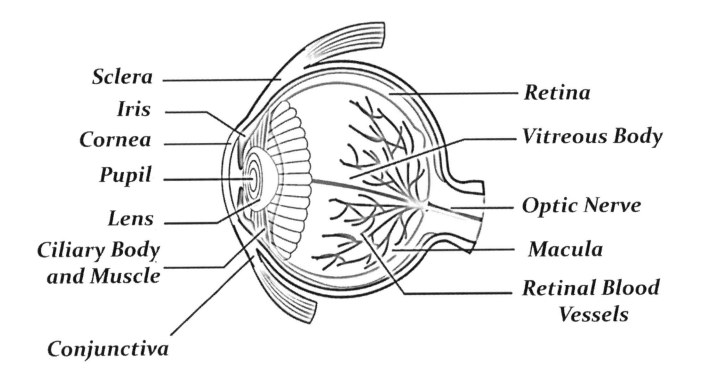

Sclera

Iris

Cornea

Pupil

Lens

Ciliary Body
and Muscle

Conjunctiva

Retina

Vitreous Body

Optic Nerve

Macula

Retinal Blood
Vessels

Diaphragm Functions in Breathing

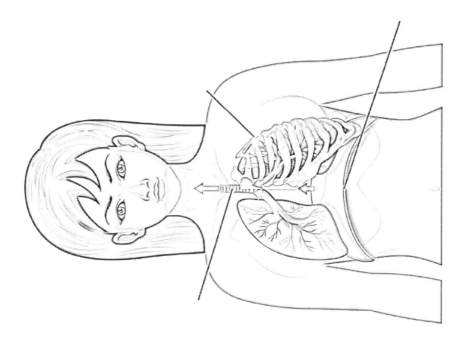

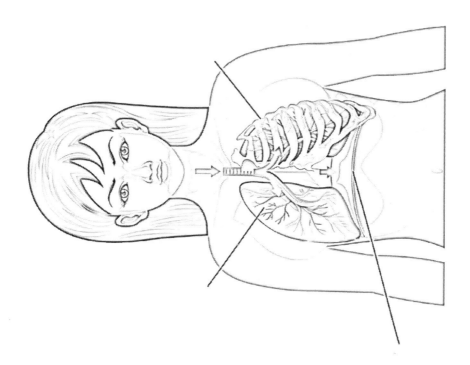

Diaphragm Functions in Breathing

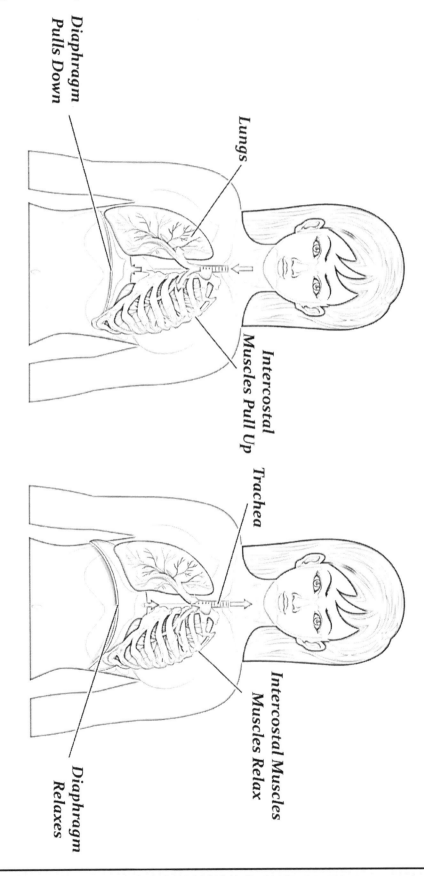

Human Respiratory System

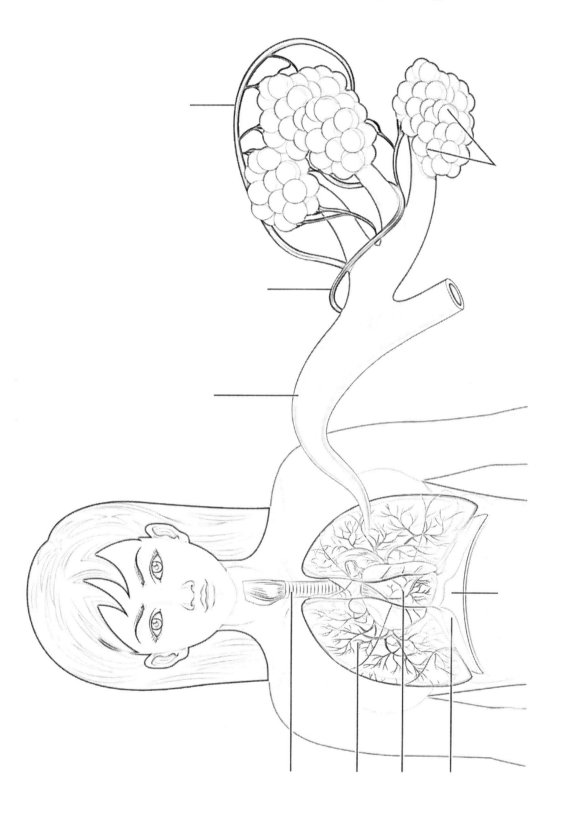

Human Respiratory System

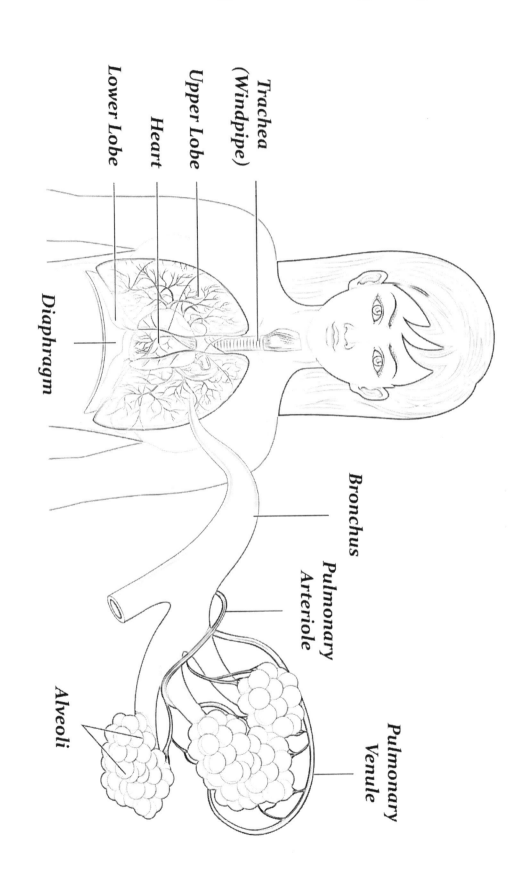

Trachea
(Windpipe)

Upper Lobe

Heart

Lower Lobe

Diaphragm

Bronchus

Pulmonary
Arteriole

Pulmonary
Venule

Alveoli

Bronchiole and Alveoli

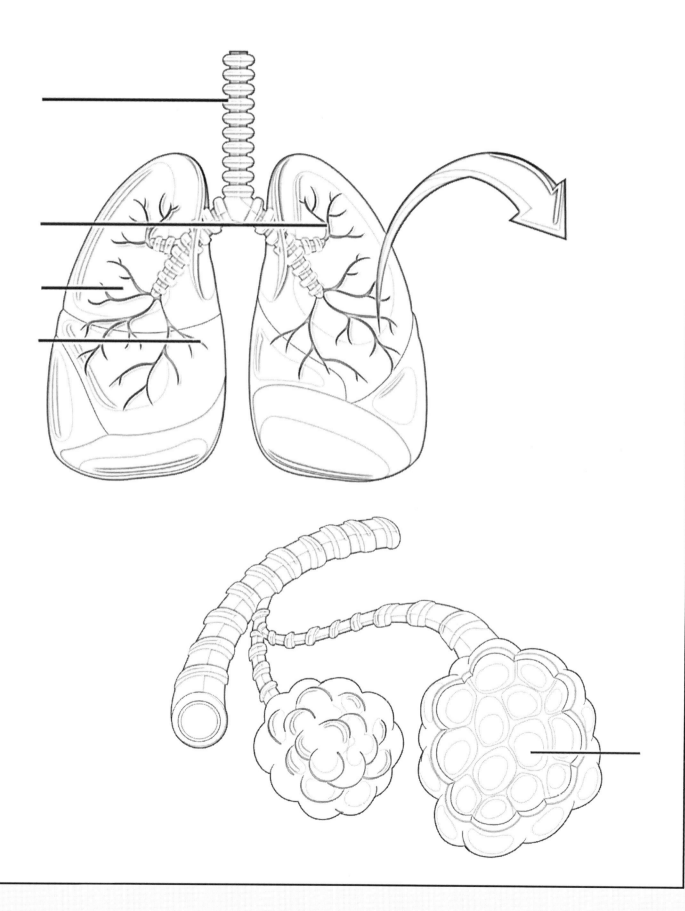

Bronchiole and Alveoli

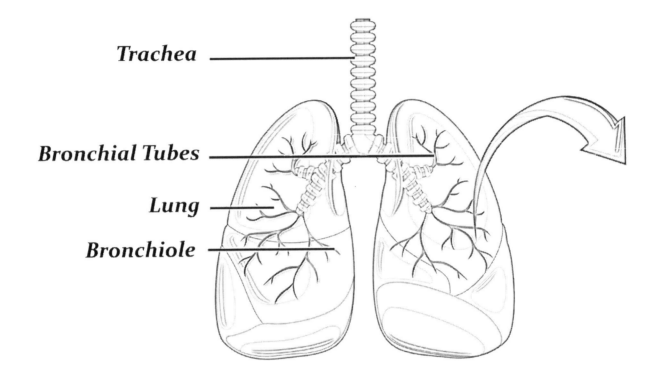

Trachea

Bronchial Tubes

Lung

Bronchiole

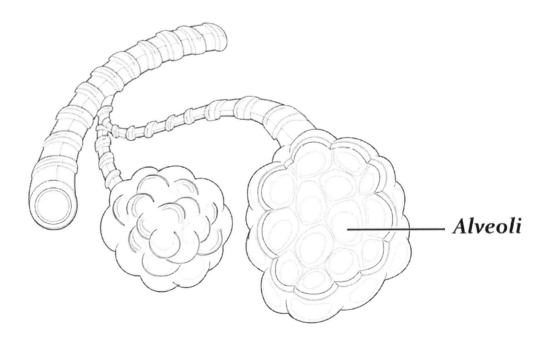

Alveoli

Pneumonia of the Lungs

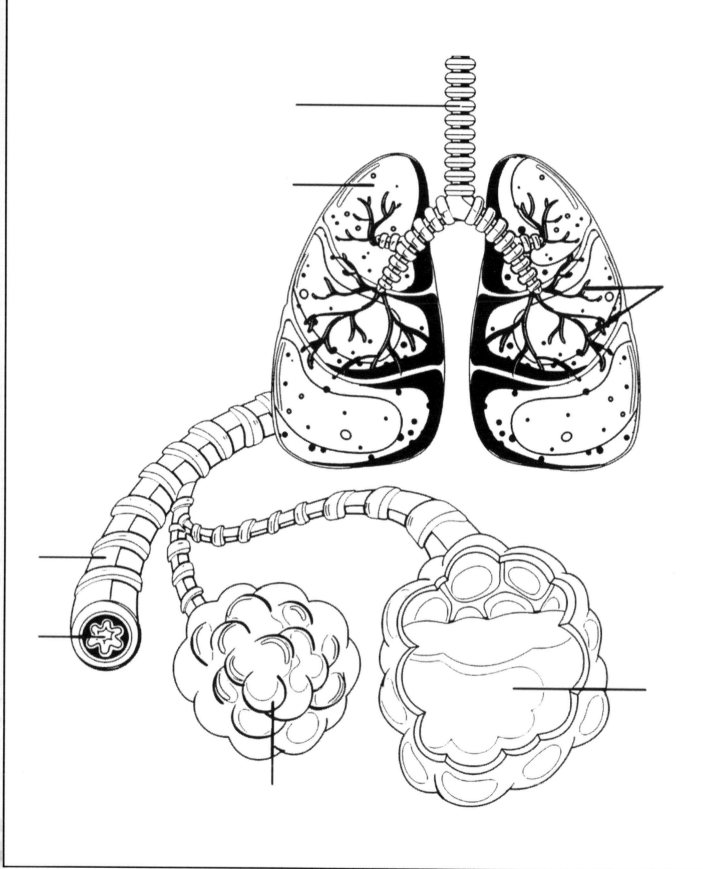

Pneumonia of the Lungs

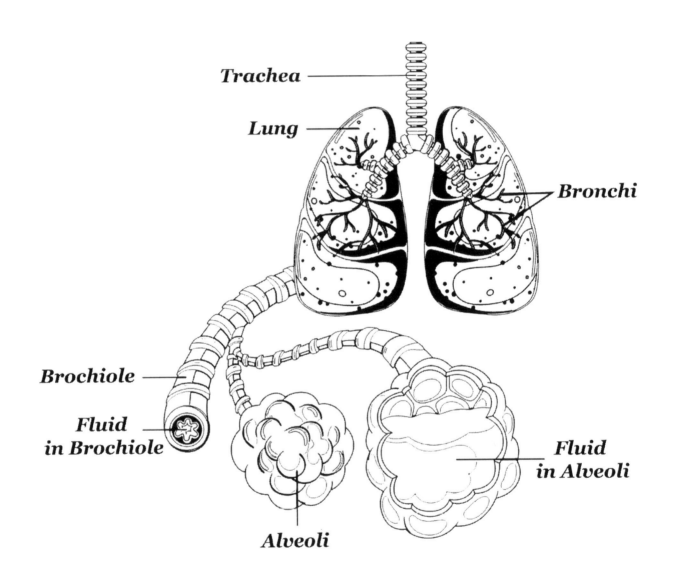

Trachea

Lung

Bronchi

Brochiole

Fluid
in Brochiole

Alveoli

Fluid
in Alveoli

Bones of the Arm and Shoulder

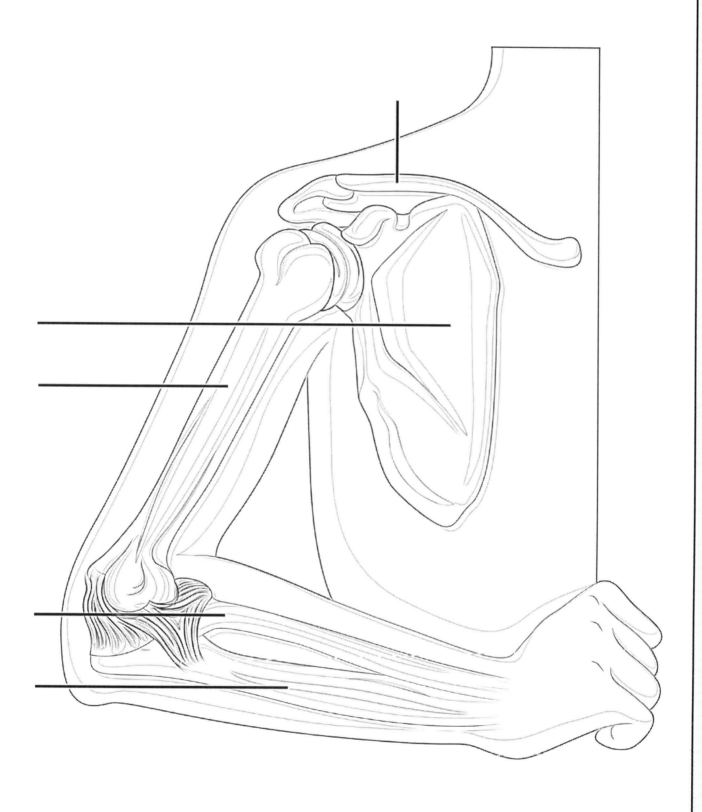

Bones of the Arm and Shoulder

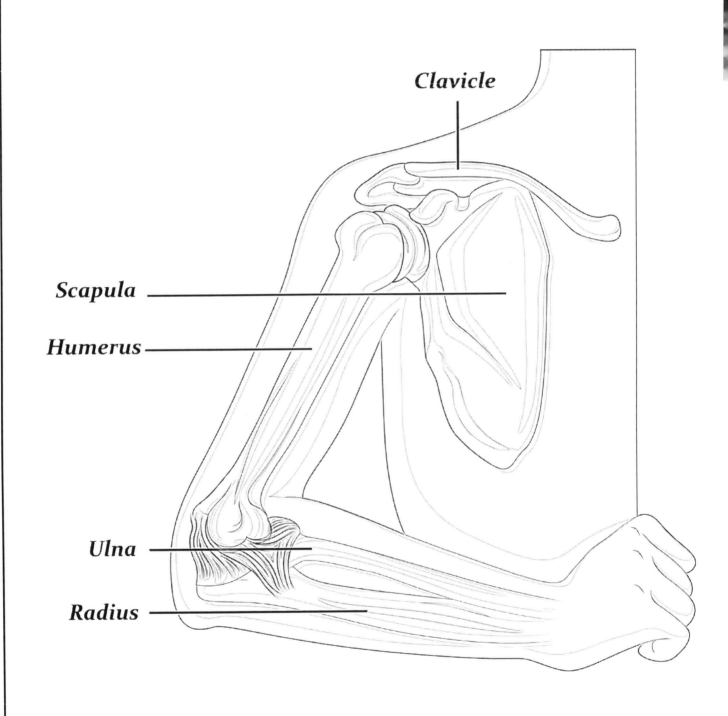

Clavicle

Scapula

Humerus

Ulna

Radius

Muscles, Nerves and Bones of the Wrist

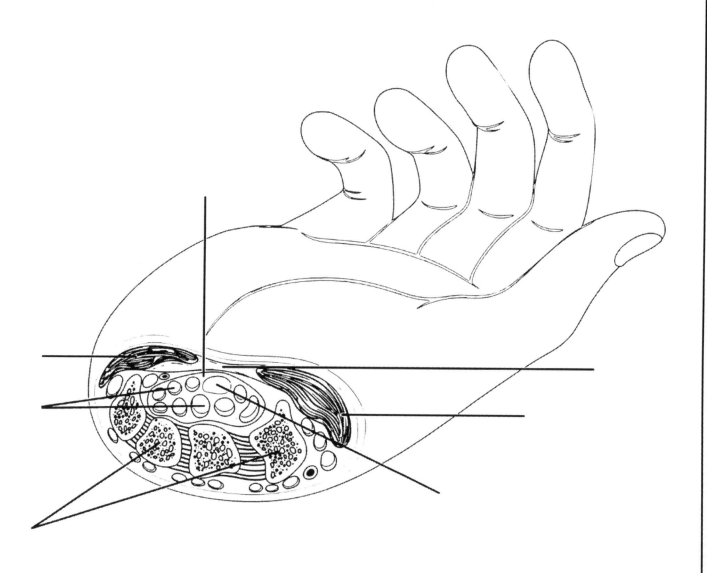

Muscles, Nerves and Bones of the Wrist

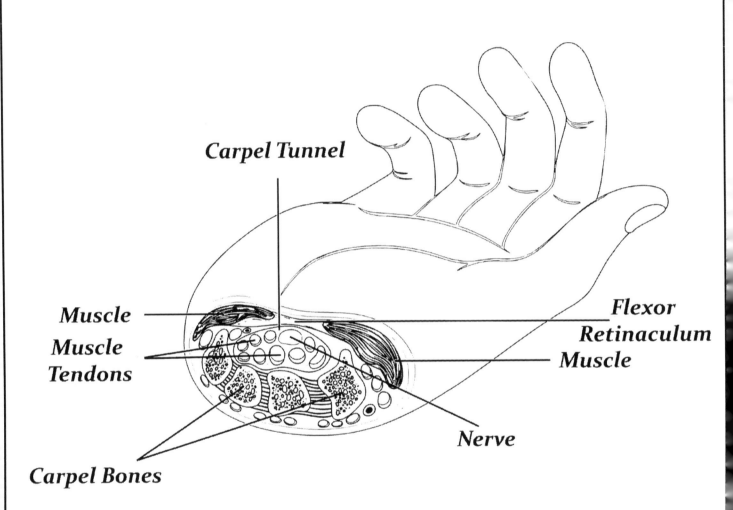

Carpel Tunnel

Muscle

Muscle
Tendons

Flexor
Retinaculum

Muscle

Nerve

Carpel Bones

Rheumatoid Arthritis in Hand

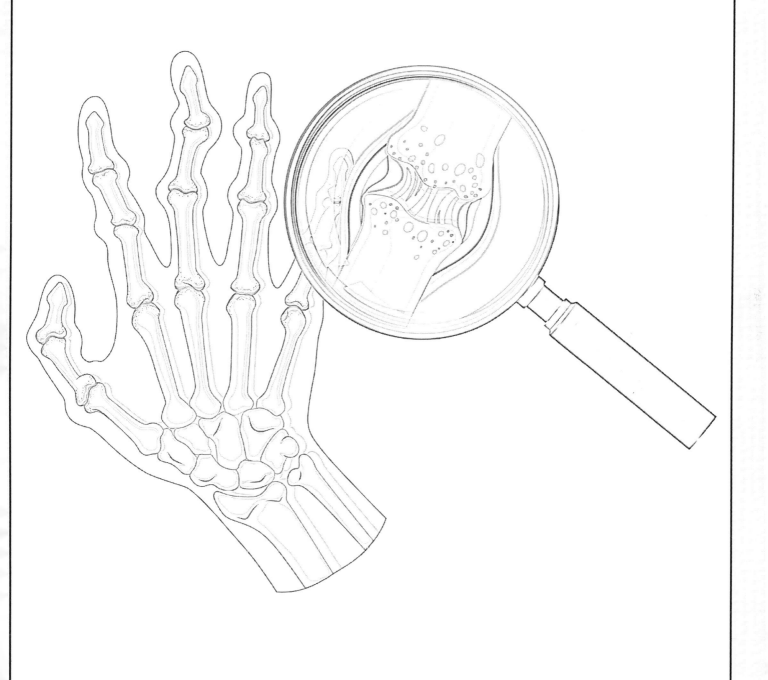

Female Reproductive System

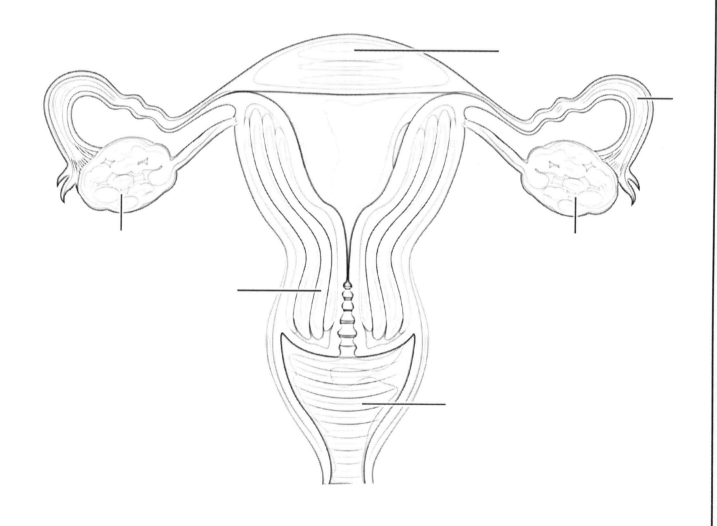

Female Reproductive System

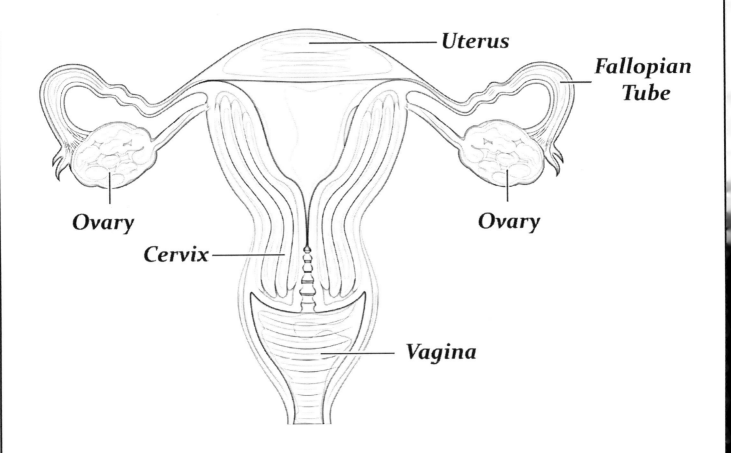

Uterus

Fallopian Tube

Ovary

Ovary

Cervix

Vagina

Male Reproductive System

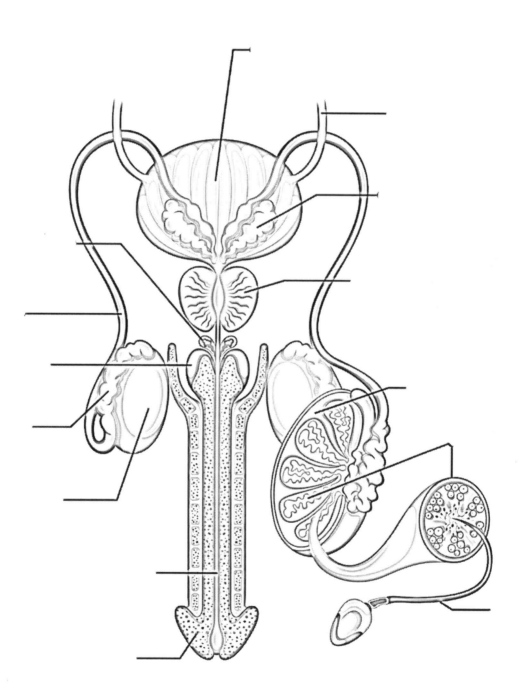

Male Reproductive System

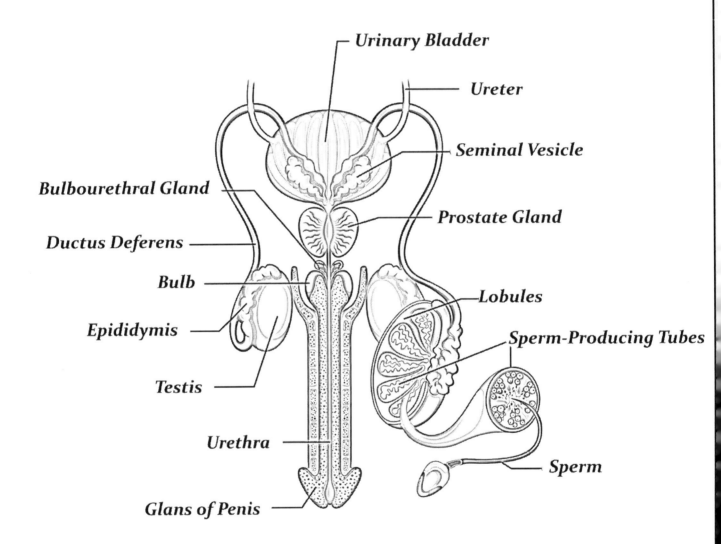

- Urinary Bladder
- Ureter
- Seminal Vesicle
- Bulbourethral Gland
- Prostate Gland
- Ductus Deferens
- Bulb
- Lobules
- Epididymis
- Sperm-Producing Tubes
- Testis
- Urethra
- Sperm
- Glans of Penis

Male Reproductive System

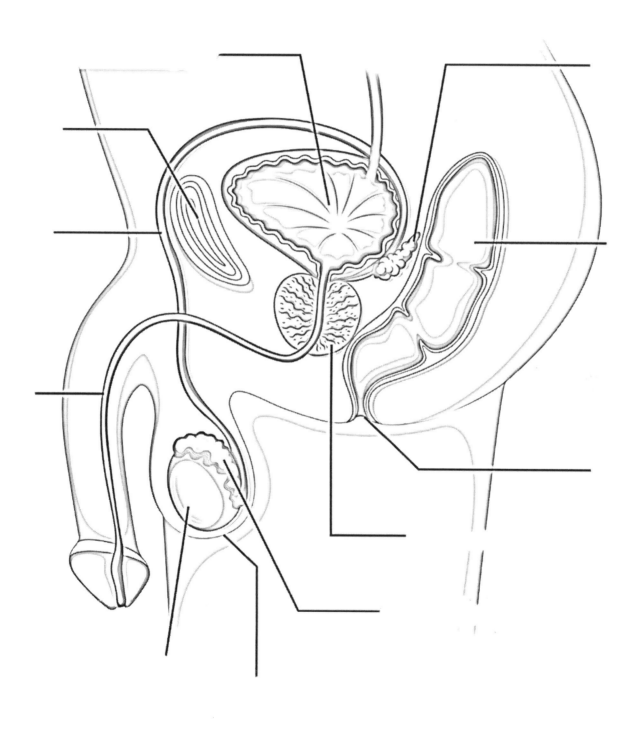

Male Reproductive System

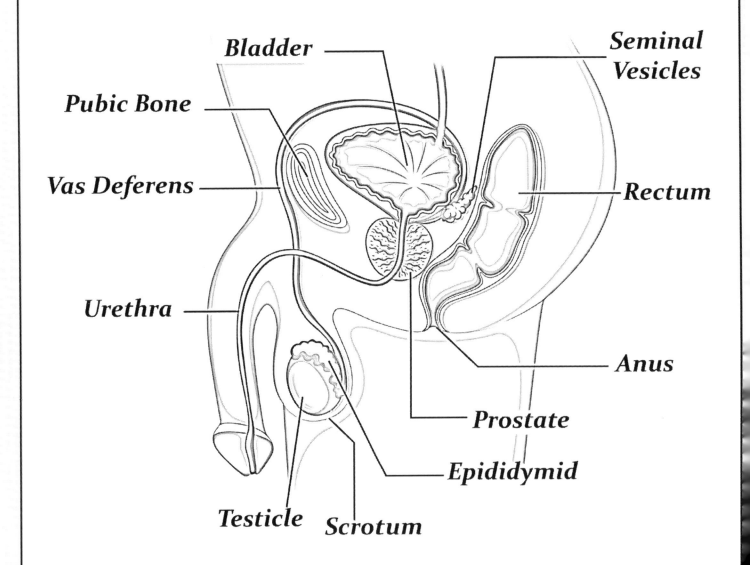

Bladder

Pubic Bone

Vas Deferens

Urethra

Seminal Vesicles

Rectum

Anus

Prostate

Epididymid

Testicle Scrotum

Human Kidneys and Bladder

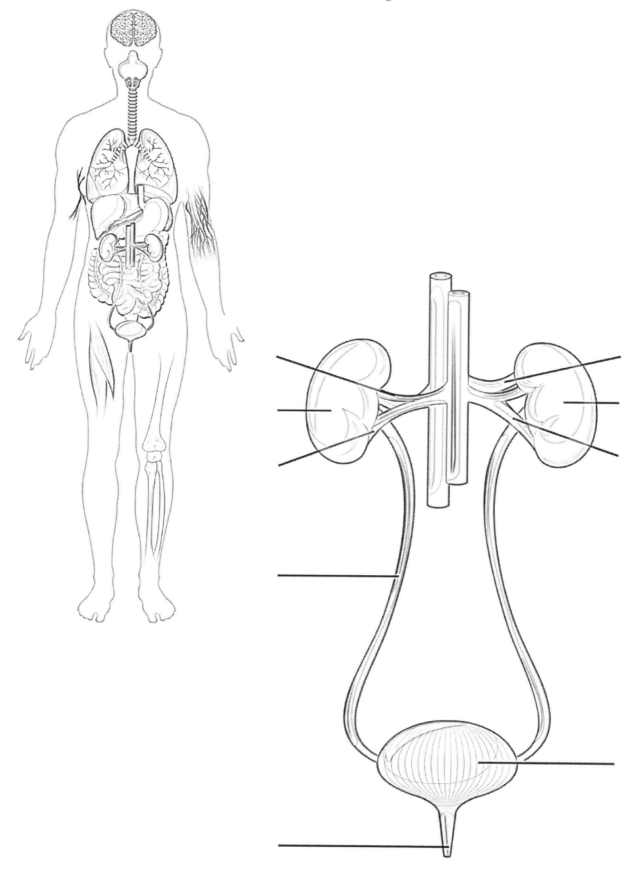

Human Kidneys and Bladder

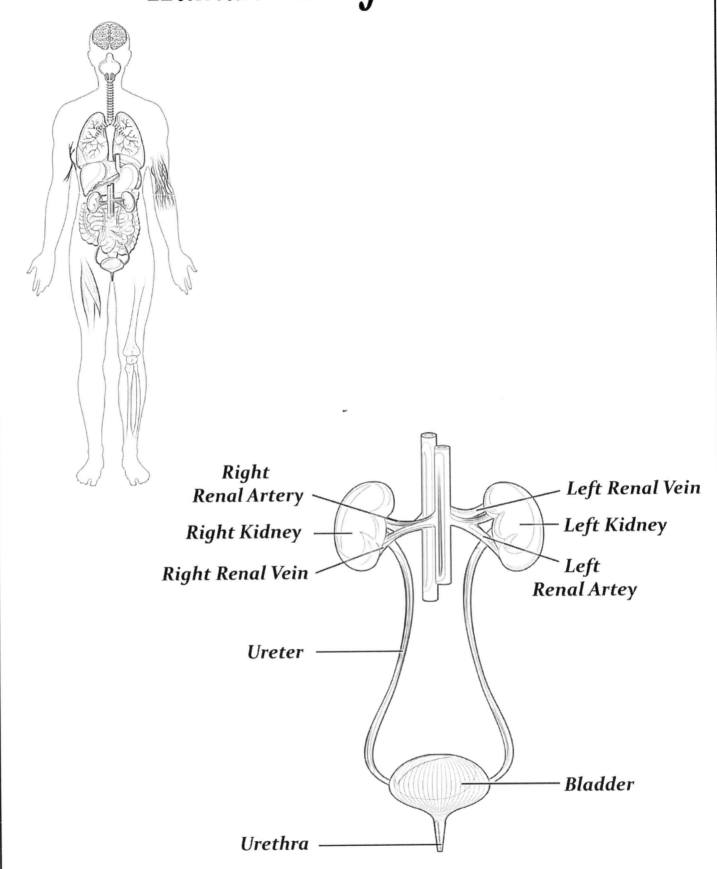

Right
Renal Artery

Right Kidney

Right Renal Vein

Left Renal Vein

Left Kidney

Left
Renal Artey

Ureter

Bladder

Urethra

Human Kidney Stones

Healthy Kidney

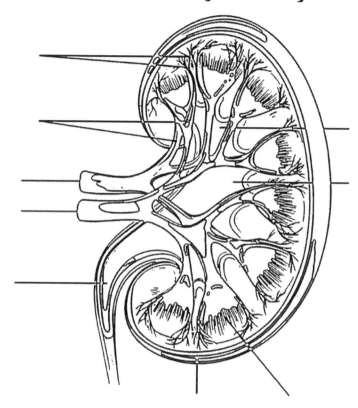

Kidney with Kidney Stones

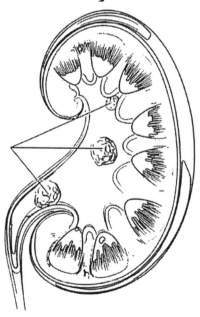

Human Kidney Stones

Healthy Kidney

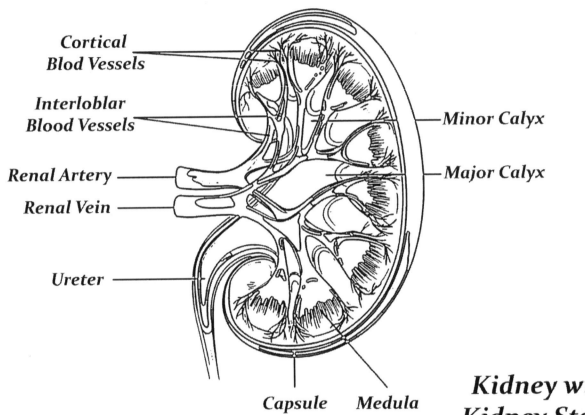

Cortical
Blod Vessels

Interloblar
Blood Vessels

Renal Artery

Renal Vein

Ureter

Capsule   Medula

Minor Calyx

Major Calyx

Kidney with
Kidney Stones

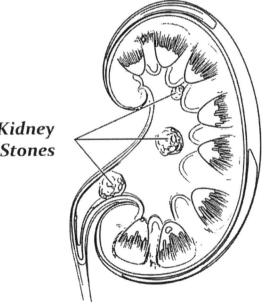

Kidney
Stones

Human Gas Exchange Process

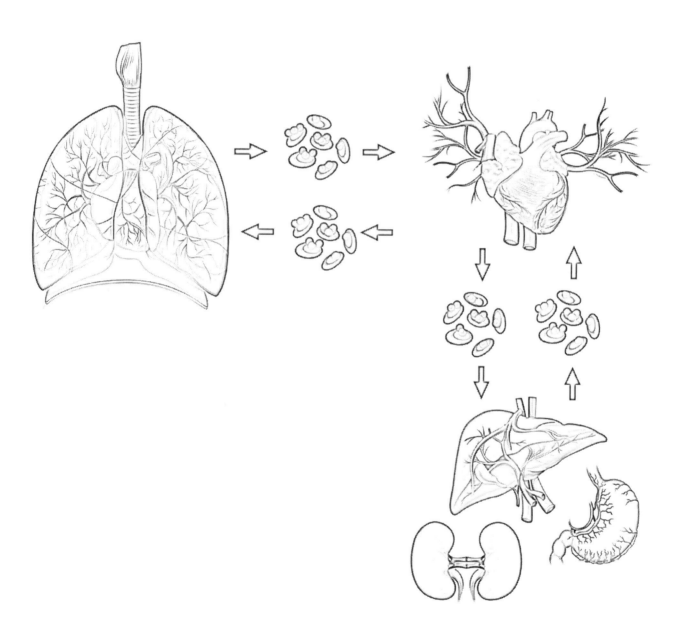

Human Gas Exchange Process

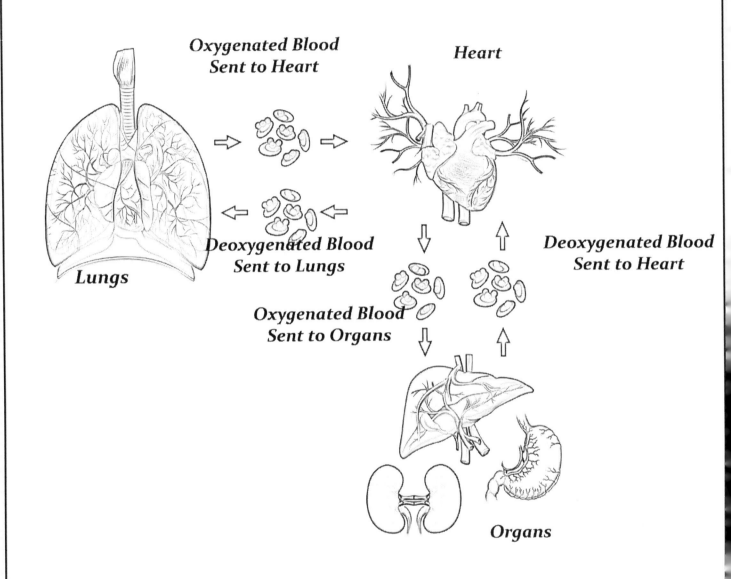

Rib Cage

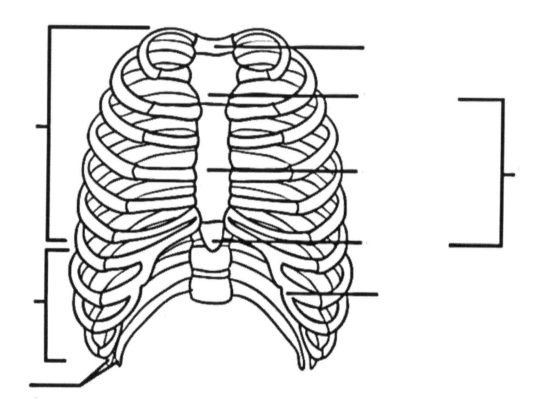

Rib Cage

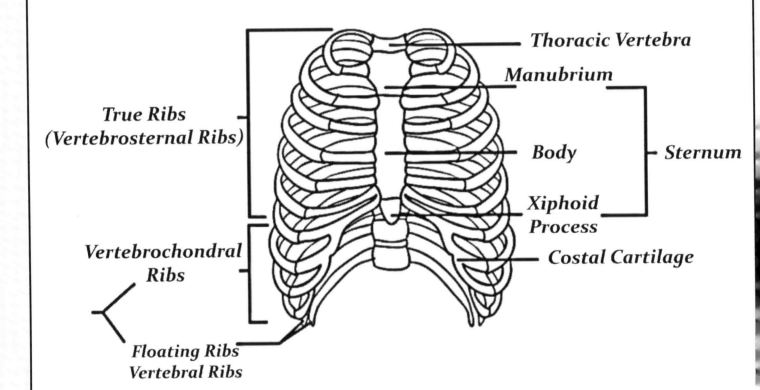

True Ribs
(Vertebrosternal Ribs)

Vertebrochondral
Ribs

Floating Ribs
Vertebral Ribs

Thoracic Vertebra

Manubrium

Body

Sternum

Xiphoid
Process

Costal Cartilage

Strangulated Ernia

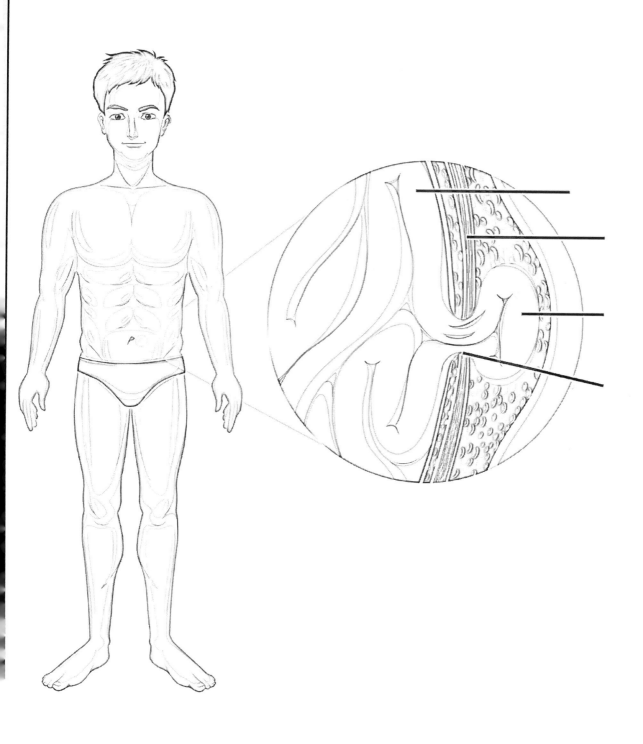

Strangulated Ernia

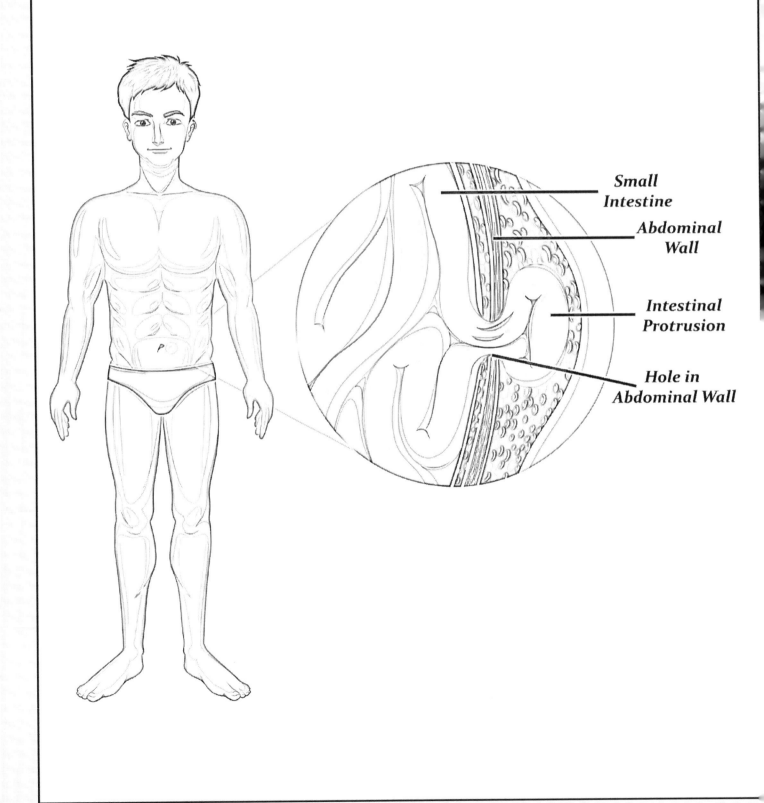

Small Intestine

Abdominal Wall

Intestinal Protrusion

Hole in Abdominal Wall

Human Skin and Hair

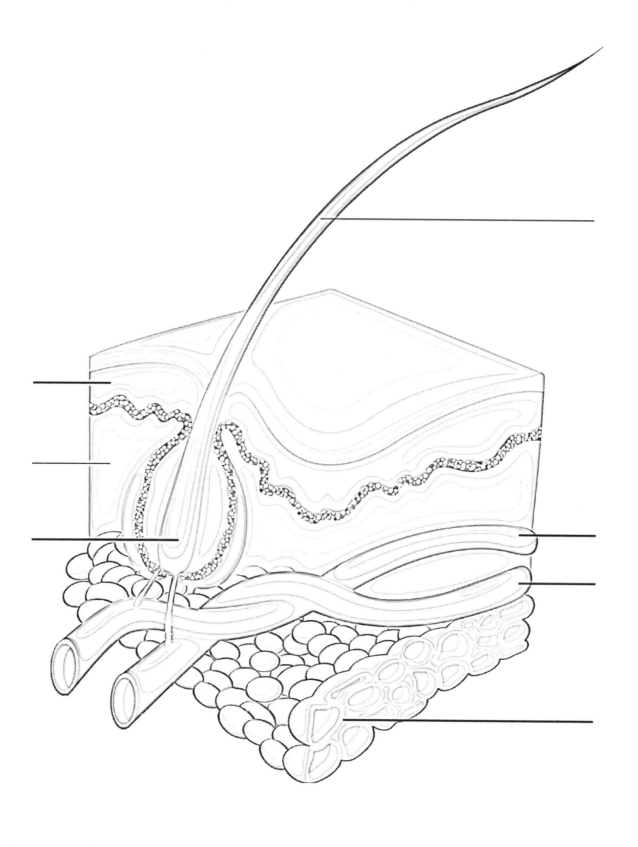

Human Skin and Hair

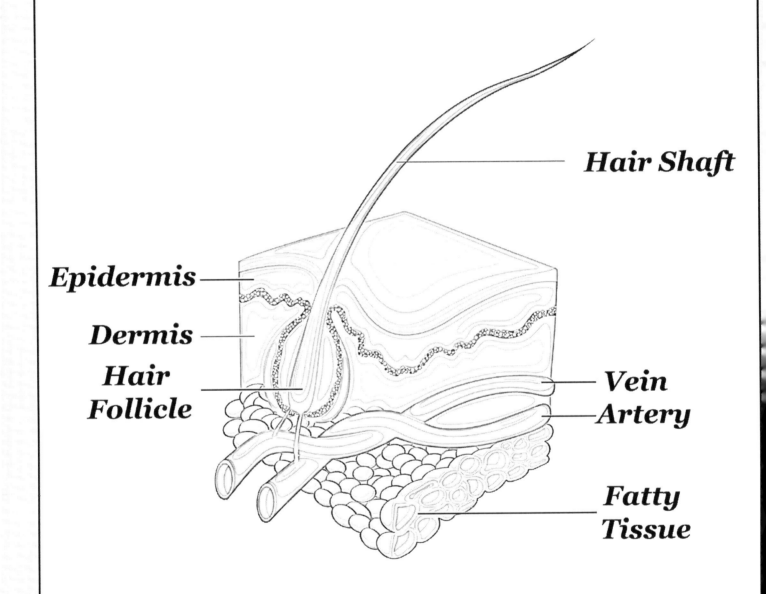

Hair Shaft

Epidermis

Dermis

Hair
Follicle

Vein

Artery

Fatty
Tissue

Types of Fractures

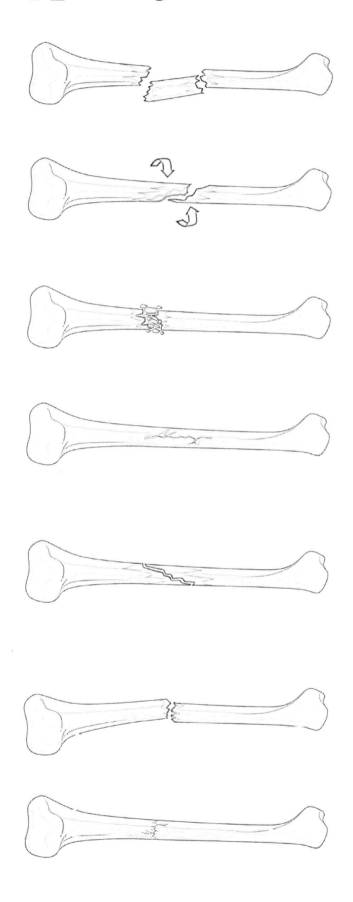

Types of Fractures

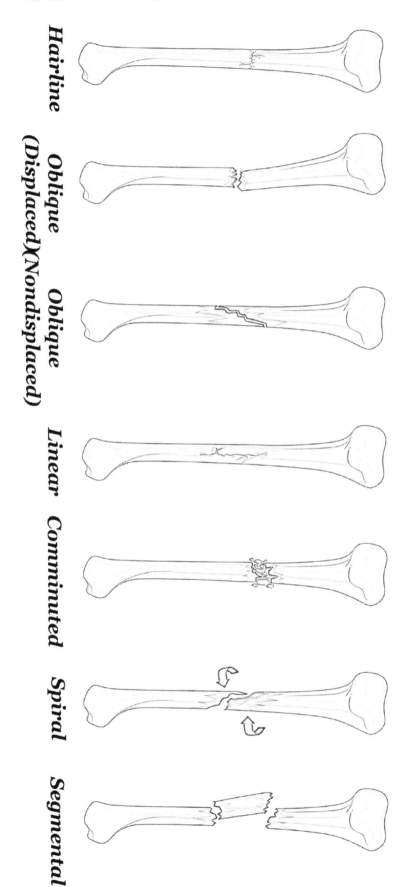

Symptoms of Lupus Erythematosus

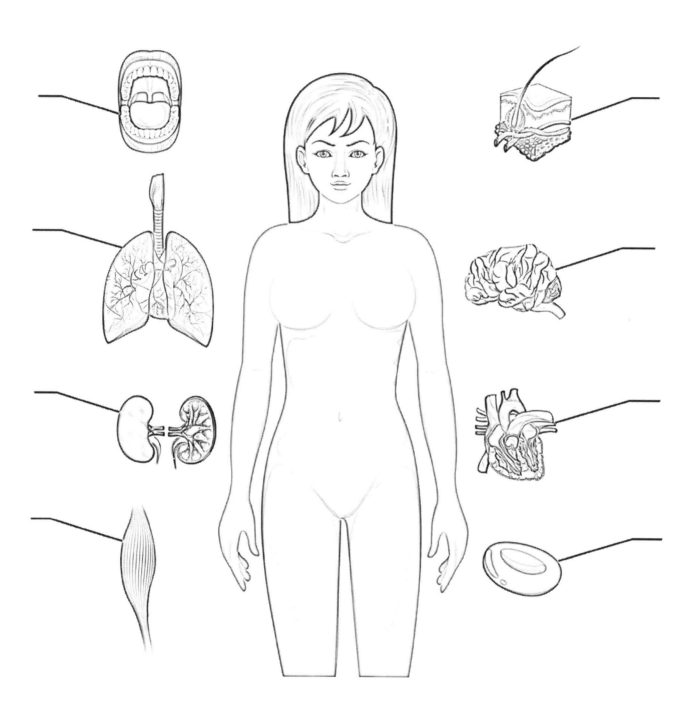

Symptoms of Lupus Erythematosus

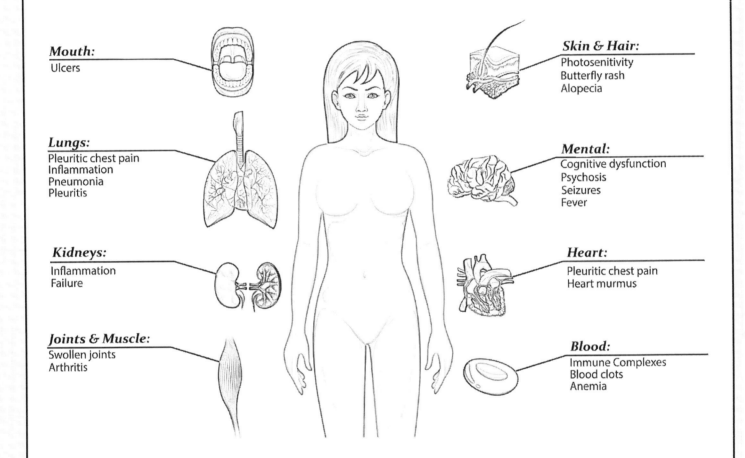

Mouth:
Ulcers

Lungs:
Pleuritic chest pain
Inflammation
Pneumonia
Pleuritis

Kidneys:
Inflammation
Failure

Joints & Muscle:
Swollen joints
Arthritis

Skin & Hair:
Photosenitivity
Butterfly rash
Alopecia

Mental:
Cognitive dysfunction
Psychosis
Seizures
Fever

Heart:
Pleuritic chest pain
Heart murmur

Blood:
Immune Complexes
Blood clots
Anemia

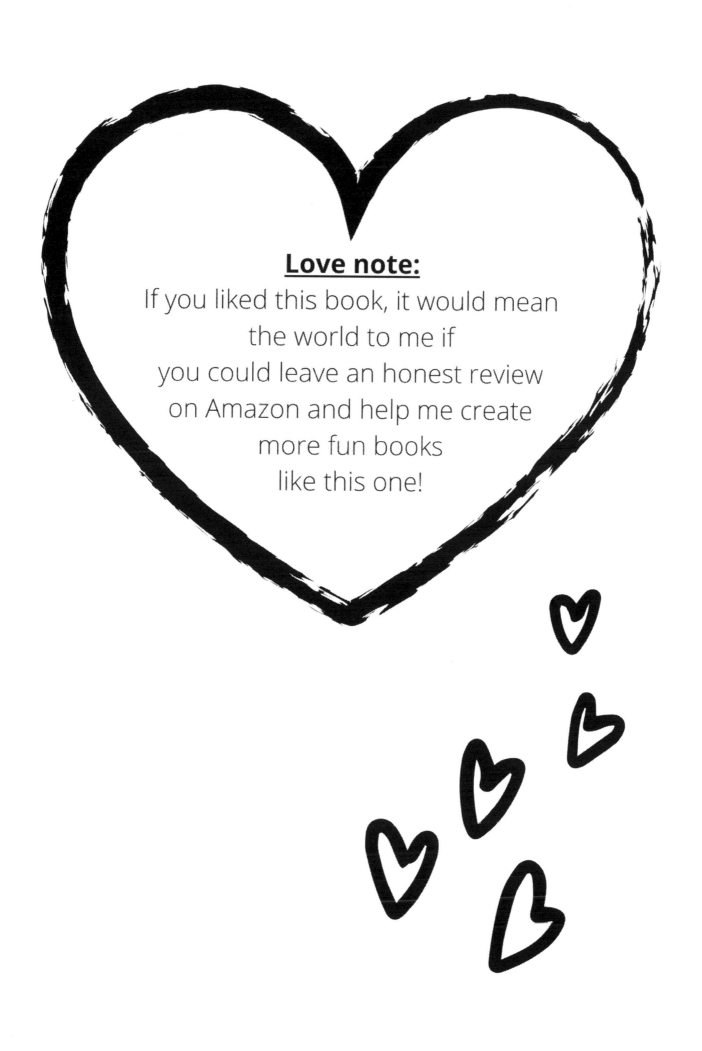

<u>Love note:</u>
If you liked this book, it would mean
the world to me if
you could leave an honest review
on Amazon and help me create
more fun books
like this one!

Made in the USA
Columbia, SC
20 August 2024

40814114R00035